RAINBOW CLASSICS

General Editor: May Lamberton Becker

THE RAINBOW
Mother Goose

Edited, with an Introduction, by

May Lamberton Becker

Illustrated by Lili Cassel

Cleveland and New York

The World Publishing Company

Rainbow Classics

are published by THE WORLD PUBLISHING COMPANY

2231 West 110th Street · Cleveland 2 · Ohio

Contents

5

PART TWO. *Mother Goose's Favorite Alphabet Poems and Rhymes about Counting, the Days, the Months, and the Weather*

8

PART THREE. *Mother Goose's Favorite Puzzles, Games, Tongue-twisters and Wise Sayings*

Introduction

TO THE PARENTS

by May Lamberton Becker

As Mother Goose comes to children long before reading sets in, the Introduction to this book of melodies is not addressed to the child who will receive it, but to the grownup who will read it to him. For though this grownup will enjoy—perhaps as much as the little person—a chance to present to his child these friends of his early childhood, this enjoyment may be heightened, and admiration and respect added to it, by bearing in mind several points on which he was uninformed when he first met Mother Goose.

First, by introducing your child to Mother Goose's characters you make him a friend of some of the liveliest people in English literature. They bounce with vitality. You meet them for a moment and remember them forever. Indeed, you will be continually reminded of them in all sorts of ways, from colored advertisements to political parodies and editorial comment; often, you would have missed the point of an allusion had you not known who Cock Robin was, or what the Knave of Hearts did, or why Jack Horner thought himself such a good boy. It is a lifelong handicap if you do not know these people, as the English-speaking world takes it for granted that you do. I noticed several years ago that this handicap can be felt early in life. A shop famous for its window displays put on a panorama of moving figures, each group representing scenes from Mother Goose. These came into sight through a little door at the left of the show window, and an eager crowd of city children, blocking the pavement clear to the curb, greeted each one by name before it was

11

half way through the entrance. "There's Simple Simon!" they cried; or "Here come Jack and Jill!" They were all one, that crowd of children, in this merry moment of recognition—all except one little fellow seated high on his father's shoulder. He didn't know the name of a single figure. He kept leaning down to ask Papa, but by the time Papa had answered him the figure had passed. The little chap was completely out of it. I hope Papa bought him the book on the way home, as an apology for not doing his duty sooner.

In the second place, as you now read these rhymes you can see how dramatic they are. The best of them are little dramas, whose rules require—as you learned in your study of playwriting —that characters must be introduced as soon as possible, and that action, beginning at once, should rise steadily to a climax not long before the end, and then coast down swiftly to the final curtain. Now run over a typical Mother Goose rhyme and you will see that this is just what it does. The first words tell you who the hero is, and what he does rises rapidly to a climax and then glides down to an ending.

If you make a Mother Goose rhyme into a diagram you will see that it has the shape of a well-made play:

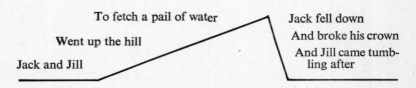

Of course, you don't tell all this to a little child; he's not ready for dramatic criticism. But if you bear it in mind while reciting these little dramas to a child, you'll get more vivid effect from your performance.

Indeed, if you intend to tell stories of your own to very little children, or to write them, you can't do better than keep Mother Goose's method in mind. Let your reader or your listener know, first of all, the name of the child your story is about; give the

12

child something to do that swiftly gets more interesting as it goes on, and bring this action to its high spot just in time to come down to a firm landing on the last page. And though you will not match the condensation of these miniature masterpieces, let it remind you to keep your story short.

I trust that in reading these rhymes aloud you will not only recover old favorites but discover several that were not in the book you had as a child. Perhaps some of those you remember from that book may not be in this one. That is because no one person wrote them all, nor were they all composed at one time—indeed, you can tell by the way they sound that they must have been sung or recited before they were written at all. From time to time such collections have been made: the name common to them all comes from Perrault's *Contes de Ma Mère l'Oye*, which was translated from the French into English in 1729, though Mother Goose—"Ma Mère l'Oye"—probably had a traditional existence much earlier. Sir Walter Scott believed he had traced her to a period of remote antiquity in Italy—perhaps to her origin at Naples. The first collection made for English children appeared in 1744, the year of the opening of the shop of John Newbery, the Eighteenth Century London bookseller whom all lovers of children's literature still delight to honor; it was called *Tommy Thumb's Pretty Song Book*. The only surviving copy of this little book is now in the British Museum: it measures three by one and one-half inches. Francis Power, Newbery's grandson, published *Mother Goose's Melody: or, Sonnets for the Cradle* in 1791, and in Worcester, Massachusetts, Isaiah Thomas brought out a third edition of his own *Mother Goose's Melody* in 1799. You will find this data, and more, in F. C. Harvey-Darton's *Children's Books in England*. The best authority has it that no true parentage can be found for the rhymes, and no one book is likely to hold all that have been gathered in all the collections. You could no more have a Definitive Edition of Mother Goose than you could have a definitive edition of the telephone book. They both keep on growing.

Some of the rhymes have undoubtedly grown out of historical

13

events, and refer to people whose real names are famous. Children's games often keep an event alive long after what they commemorate has been forgotten. Little children in a New York street can sing that London Bridge is broken down, build it up with silver and gold, and hold prisoners one by one for ransom, without a notion that they are acting out something that happened a long time ago. No doubt many of these rhymes are about such things long forgotten; all we really need to bear in mind is that a typical verse from Mother Goose comes to us from far back. The little chap who recites "Humpty Dumpty" before he can "talk plain" would not be interested in the possibility that the original humpback to have "a great fall" may have been Richard III, or that Old King Cole was the legendary monarch for whom Colchester was named. A three-year-old doesn't know there is such a thing as history. But learned men have not thought it beneath them to trace the origins of these gay little verses; they have found that in the beginning they were often the only safe way to laugh at exalted personages. Into conjecture this Introduction cannot go: it takes space to disentangle facts from guesswork; but I like to think that the Frog who would "a-wooing go" may have been the elderly Queen Elizabeth's young French suitor, the Duc d'Anjou, whom she and the court found so amusing; and it seems to me that "I love sixpence" hits off the ruling passion of Henry VIII so neatly that his subjects knew whom they meant when they sang it.

These bright, fresh verses have been here a long while, yet each generation of babies finds them waiting, old as yesterday and new as tomorrow. They have outlasted brick and stone; many houses have fallen from old age while the House that Jack built has been standing firm. Fire and flying bombs have gutted London churches, but their steeples still sing in "Gay go up and gay go down, to ring the bells of London town." And though the loveliest of them stands stark and voiceless on its island in the Strand, the sound of its bells will linger as long as children chant "Oranges and lemons, say the bells of St. Clement's."

Lili Cassel, who illustrated this edition of *Mother Goose*, is

such a small person that she looks as if she might have stepped
out of one of her own delightful drawings (perhaps the one for
"I Had a Little Hen," or the one for "If").   She has large brown
eyes and a great deal of dark, curly hair, and to look at her you
would never realize that she is a young lady in her middle twen-
ties.   She says that her idea in illustrating *Mother Goose* was to
make the pictures modern and American.   Many of her gay and
pretty sketches of little girls and boys were drawn from life, from
among the children in the suburb of Kew Gardens, where she
lives, and from among the children in New York City, where she
works.

Mother Goose is the first book which Miss Cassel has illustrated, but she is by no means a newcomer to the art world. She
has worked as the assistant to a designer of ads and posters, in
an advertising agency, and in the promotion art department of
Time magazine.   She has also done many book jackets.   It seems
to me appropriate that she should have drawn the pictures for
this book, not only because her hobbies are collecting children's
books and drawing pictures of young people, but because
through her own youth she has been able to capture in picture
form the perennial youthfulness of these enduring rhymes.

PART ONE

Mother Goose's Favorite
Poems and Lullabies

Old Mother Goose

Old Mother Goose, when
She wanted to wander,
Would ride through the air
On a very fine gander.

Little Miss Muffet

Little Miss Muffet
Sat on a tuffet,
Eating her curds and whey;

There came a great spider,
And sat down beside her,
And frightened Miss Muffet away.

19

Little Bo-Peep

Little Bo-Peep has lost her sheep
And can't tell where to find them.
Leave them alone and they will come home
Bringing their tails behind them.

Humpty Dumpty

Humpty Dumpty sat on a wall,
Humpty Dumpty had a great fall;
All the King's horses, and all the King's men
Cannot put Humpty Dumpty together again.

Little Boy Blue

Little Boy Blue, come blow your horn,

The sheep's in the meadow, the cow's in the
    corn.

Where is the boy that looks after the sheep?
He's under the haycock, fast asleep.

Jack and Jill

Jack and Jill went up the hill,
　To fetch a pail of water;
Jack fell down, and broke his crown,
　And Jill came tumbling after.

Then up Jack got and off did trot,
  As fast as he could caper,
To old Dame Dob, who patched his nob
  With vinegar and brown paper.

Mary's Lamb

Mary had a little lamb,
  Its fleece was white as snow;
And everywhere that Mary went
  The lamb was sure to go.

It followed her to school one day:
  Which was against the rule;
It made the children laugh and play
  To see a lamb at school.

And so the teacher turned it out,
  But still it lingered near,
And waited patiently about
  Till Mary did appear.

"What makes the lamb love Mary so?"
  The eager children cry.
"Why, Mary loves the lamb, you know,"
  The teacher did reply.

Baa, Baa, Black Sheep

Baa, baa, black sheep, have you any wool?
Yes, sir; yes, sir—three bags full:
One for the master, one for the dame,
One for the little boy that lives in our lane.

Little Jack Horner

Little Jack Horner
Sat in a corner,
Eating his Christmas pie;
He put in his thumb,
And pulled out a plum,
And said, "What a good boy am I!"

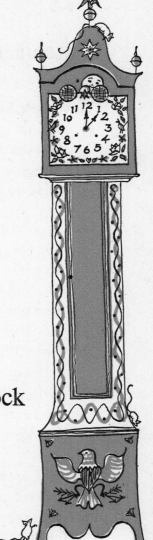

Hickory Dickory Dock

Hickory dickory dock
The mouse ran up the clock
The clock struck one
The Mouse ran down
Hickory dickory dock.

27

Three Little Kittens

Three little kittens lost their mittens,
    and they began to cry,
Oh! mother dear,
We very much fear
That we have lost our mittens.

Lost your mittens! You naughty kittens!
    Then you shall have no pie.
Mee-ow, mee-ow, mee-ow.
No, you shall have no pie.
Mee-ow, mee-ow, mee-ow.

The three little kittens found their mittens,
    and they began to cry,
Oh! mother dear,
See here, see here!
See, we have found our mittens.

Put on your mittens, you silly kittens,
    and you shall have some pie.
Purr-r, purr-r, purr-r,
    Oh! let us have the pie!
    Purr-r, purr-r, purr-r.

Mary, Mary, Quite Contrary

Mary, Mary, quite contrary,
  How does your garden grow?
With cockle-shells and silver bells
  And pretty maids all in a row.

Sing a Song of Sixpence

Sing a song of sixpence,
    A pocket full of rye;
Four-and-twenty blackbirds
    Baked in a pie!

When the pie was opened
    The birds began to sing;
Was not that a dainty dish
    To set before the king?

The king was in his counting-house,
    Counting out his money;
The queen was in the parlor,
    Eating bread and honey.

The maid was in the garden,
    Hanging out the clothes;
When down came a blackbird
    And snapped off her nose.

What Are Little Boys Made of?

What are little boys made of, made of?
What are little boys made of?
"Snaps and snails, and puppy-dogs' tails;
And that's what little boys are made of."

What are little girls made of, made of?
What are little girls made of?
"Sugar and spice, and all that's nice;
And that's what little girls are made of."

Old King Cole

Old King Cole was a merry old soul
And a merry old soul was he.
He called for his pipe,
And he called for his bowl
And he called for his fiddlers three.

Every fiddler, he had a fiddle
And a very fine fiddle had he,
Twee Tweedle Dee Tweedle Dee,
   went the fiddlers,
Oh, there's none so rare, as can compare,
With King Cole and his fiddlers three.

Polly, Put the Kettle On

Polly, put the kettle on,
Polly, put the kettle on,
Polly, put the kettle on,
And let's drink tea.

Sukey, take it off again,
Sukey, take it off again,
Sukey, take it off again,
They're all gone away.

The Little Girl with a Curl

There was a little girl who had a little curl
Right in the middle of her forehead;
When she was good, she was very, very good,
And when she was bad she was horrid.

See-saw, Sacaradown

See-saw, Sacaradown,
Which is the way to London Town?
One foot up, and the other down,
And that is the way to London Town.

Rain

Rain, rain, go away,
Come again another day;
Little Johnny wants to play.

To Market

To market, to market, to buy a fat pig,
Home again, home again, jiggety jig.
To market, to market, to buy a fat hog,
Home again, home again, jiggety jog.
To market, to market, to buy a plum bun,
Home again, home again, market is done.

Hey! Diddle Diddle

Hey! Diddle diddle
The cat and the fiddle,
The cow jumped over the moon;
The little dog laugh'd
To see such sport
And the dish ran away with the spoon.

Pussy-cat, Pussy-cat

Pussy-cat, Pussy-cat, where have you been?
I've been to London to visit the Queen.
Pussy-cat, Pussy-cat, what did you there?
I frightened a little mouse under the chair.

Peter, Peter, Pumpkin Eater

Peter, Peter, pumpkin eater.
Had a wife and couldn't keep her.
He put her in a pumpkin shell
And there he kept her very well.

Hot Cross Buns

Hot cross buns, hot cross buns,
One a penny, two a penny,
Hot cross buns.

If you have no daughters,
Give them to your sons,
One a penny, two a penny,
Hot cross buns.

Cock-a-doodle-do!

Cock-a-doodle-do!
My dame has lost her shoe,
My master's lost his fiddle-stick
And knows not what to do.

Cock-a-doodle-do!
What is my dame to do?
Till master finds his fiddle-stick,
She'll dance without her shoe.

Bye, Baby Bunting

Bye, baby bunting,
Father's gone a-hunting,
Mother's gone a-milking,
Sister's gone a-silking,
And brother's gone to buy a skin
To wrap the baby bunting in.

Sleep, Baby, Sleep

Sleep, baby, sleep,
Our cottage vale is deep:
The little lamb is on the green,
With woolly fleece so soft and clean—
Sleep, baby, sleep.

Sleep, baby, sleep,
Down where the woodbines creep;
Be always like the lamb so mild,
A kind, and sweet, and gentle child.
Sleep, baby, sleep.

Hush-a-bye

Hush-a-bye; Baby on the tree top:
When the wind blows the cradle will rock.
When the bough bends, the cradle will fall,
Down will come baby, bough, cradle and all.

Where Should a Baby Rest?

Where should a baby rest?
Where but on its mother's arm—
Where can a baby lie
Half so safe from every harm?
Lulla, lulla, lullaby,
Softly sleep, my baby;
Lulla, lulla, lullaby.
Soft, soft, my baby.

Nestle there, my lovely one!
Press to mine thy velvet cheek;
Sweetly coo, and smile, and look,
All the love thou cans't not speak.
Lulla, lulla, lullaby,
Softly sleep, my baby;
Lulla, lulla, lullaby.
Soft, soft, my baby.

There Was an Old Woman

There was an old woman
Went up in a basket
Ninety times as high as the moon.
And where she was going
I could not but ask it
For in her hand she carried a broom.

"Old woman! Old woman, old woman!"
    said I,
"Whither, oh whither, oh whither, so high."
"To sweep the cobwebs right out of the sky,
    And I'll be with you by-and-by."

Little Tom Tucker

Little Tom Tucker
  Sang for his supper.
What shall we give him?
  Brown bread and butter.
How shall he cut it
  Without e'er a knife?
How shall he marry
  Without e'er a wife?

There Was a Crooked Man

There was a crooked man,
  and he went a crooked mile;
He found a crooked sixpence
  against a crooked stile;
He bought a crooked cat,
  which caught a crooked mouse,
And they all lived together
  in a little crooked house.

Jack Be Nimble

Jack be nimble
Jack be quick.
Jack jump over
The candle-stick.

Ride a Cock Horse to
Banbury Cross

Ride a cock horse to Banbury Cross
To see a fine lady on a white horse.
With rings on her fingers and bells on her toes,
She shall have music wherever she goes.

Twinkle, Twinkle

Twinkle, twinkle, little star,
How I wonder what you are!
Up above the world so high
Like a diamond in the sky!

When the blazing sun is gone,
When he nothing shines upon,
Then you show your little light,
Twinkle, twinkle, all the night.

Then the traveller in the dark
Thanks you for your tiny spark;
How could he see where to go,
If you did not twinkle so?

In the dark blue sky you keep,
Often through my curtains peep,
For you never shut your eye,
Till the sun is in the sky.

As your bright and tiny spark
Lights the traveller in the dark,
Though I know not what you are,
Twinkle, twinkle, little star.

Deedle Deedle Dumpling

Deedle Deedle Dumpling, my son John
Went to bed with his trousers on
One shoe off and one shoe on.
Deedle Deedle Dumpling, my son John.

Bobby Shaftoe

Bobby Shaftoe's gone to sea,
With silver buckles on his knee:
He'll come back and marry me,
   Pretty Bobby Shaftoe!
Bobby Shaftoe's fat and fair,
Combing down his yellow hair;
He's my love for evermore,
   Pretty Bobby Shaftoe!

This Is the House That Jack Built

This is the house that Jack built.

This is the malt
That lay in the house that Jack built.

This is the rat
That ate the malt
That lay in the house that Jack built.

This is the cat
That killed the rat
That ate the malt
That lay in the house that Jack built.

This is the dog
That worried the cat
That killed the rat
That ate the malt
That lay in the house that Jack built.

This is the cow with the crumpled horn
That tossed the dog
That worried the cat
That killed the rat
That ate the malt
That lay in the house that Jack built.

This is the maiden, all forlorn,
That milked the cow with the crumpled horn
That tossed the dog
That worried the cat
That killed the rat
That ate the malt
That lay in the house that Jack built.

This is the man, all tattered and torn,
That kissed the maiden, all forlorn,
That milked the cow with the crumpled horn
That tossed the dog
That worried the cat
That killed the rat
That ate the malt
That lay in the house that Jack built.

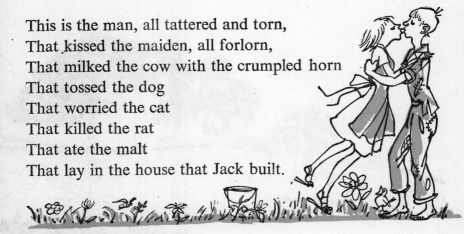

This is the priest, all shaven and shorn,
That married the man, all tattered and torn,
That kissed the maiden, all forlorn,
That milked the cow with the crumpled horn
That tossed the dog
That worried the cat
That killed the rat
That ate the malt
That lay in the house that Jack built.

This is the cock that crowed in the morn
And waked the priest, all shaven and shorn,
That married the man, all tattered and torn,
That kissed the maiden, all forlorn,
That milked the cow with the crumpled horn
That tossed the dog
That worried the cat
That killed the rat
That ate the malt
That lay in the house that Jack built.

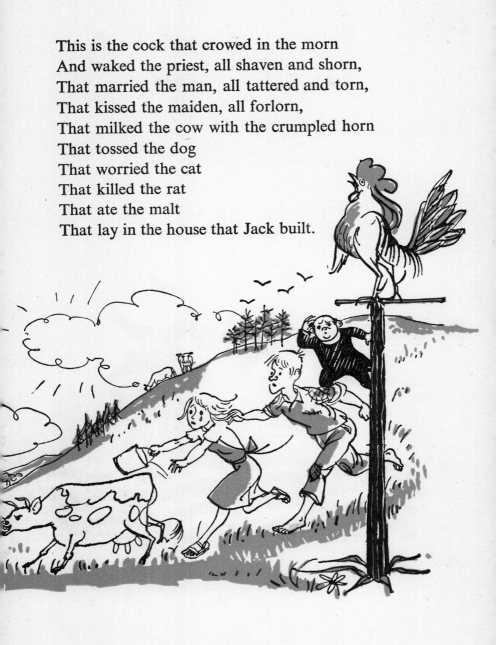

Rub-a-dub-dub

Rub-a-dub-dub,
Three men in a tub;
And who do you think they be?
The butcher, the baker,
The candlestick-maker.
They all jumped out of a rotten potato,
Turn 'hem out, knaves all three.

Taffy Was a Welshman

Taffy was a Welshman, Taffy was a thief;
   Taffy came to my house, and stole a piece of
   beef.
I went to Taffy's house, Taffy was not home;
   Taffy came to my house, and stole a marrow-
   bone.
I went to Taffy's house, Taffy was in bed;
   I took up a broomstick and flung it at his
   head.

Georgie Porgie Pudding and Pie

Georgie Porgie Pudding and Pie,
Kissed the girls and made them cry.
When the boys came out to play
Georgie Porgie ran away.

Curly Locks, Curly Locks

Curly locks, curly locks, wilt thou be mine?
Thou shalt not wash dishes nor yet feed the
  swine,
But sit on a cushion and sew a fine seam,
And feed upon strawberries, sugar, and cream.

Little Polly Flinders

Little Polly Flinders
    Sat among the cinders,
Warming her pretty little toes;
    Her mother came and caught her,
And whipped her little daughter
    For spoiling her nice new clothes.

Simple
Simon

Simple Simon met a pieman,
  Going to the fair;
Says Simple Simon to the pieman,
  "Let me taste your ware."

Says the pieman to Simple Simon,
  "Show me first your penny,"
Says Simple Simon to the pieman,
  "Indeed, I have not any."

Simple Simon went a-fishing
  For to catch a whale;
All the water he could find
  Was in his mother's pail!

Simple Simon went to look
    If plums grew on a thistle;
He pricked his fingers very much,
    Which made poor Simon whistle.

He went to catch a dicky bird,
    And thought he could not fail,
Because he had a little salt,
    To put upon its tail.

He went for water with a sieve,
    But soon it ran all through;
And now poor Simple Simon
    Bids you all adieu.

I Had a Little Nut Tree

I had a little nut tree, nothing would it bear
But a silver nutmeg and a golden pear;
The King of Spain's daughter came to visit me,
And all was because of my little nut tree.
I skipped over water, I danced over sea,
And all the birds in the air couldn't catch me.

Tom, Tom, the Piper's Son

Tom, Tom, the piper's son,
Stole a pig and away he run;
Pig was eat, and Tom was beat,
And Tom went roaring down the street.

If

If all the world were apple pie,
    And all the sea were ink,
And all the trees were bread and cheese,
    What should we have for drink?

Jack Sprat

Jack Sprat could eat no fat
His wife could eat no lean
And so, betwixt them both you see,
They licked the platter clean.

The Clock

There's a neat little clock,—
  In the schoolroom it stands,—
And it points to the time
  With its two little hands.

And may we, like the clock,
  Keep a face clean and bright,
With hands ever ready
  To do what is right.

A Dillar a Dollar

A dillar a dollar
A ten o'clock scholar.
Why do you come so soon?
You used to come at ten o'clock
And now you come at noon!

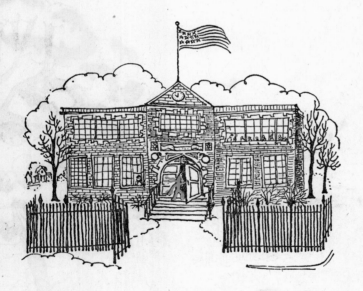

The King of France

The King of France went up the hill,
With twenty thousand men;
The King of France came down the hill,
And ne'er went up again.

The Hobby-horse

I had a little hobby-horse,
   And it was dapple gray;
Its head was made of pea-straw,
   Its tail was made of hay.

I sold it to an old woman
   For a copper groat;
And I'll not sing my song again
   Without another coat.

Three Blind Mice

Three blind mice! See how they run!
They all ran after the farmer's wife,
Who cut off their tails with a carving knife.
Did you ever see such a thing in your life
As three blind mice?

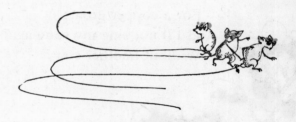

I Saw a Ship A-sailing

I saw a ship a-sailing,
   A-sailing on the sea,
And oh! it was all laden
   With pretty things for thee!

There were comfits in the cabin,
   And apples in the hold;
The sails were made of silk,
   And the masts were made of gold.

The four-and-twenty sailors
   That stood between the decks
Were four-and-twenty white mice,
   With chains about their necks.

The captain was a duck,
   With a packet on his back;
And when the ship began to move,
   The captain said "Quack! quack!"

Oh, Where, Oh, Where Is My Little Dog Gone?

Oh, where, oh, where is my little dog gone?
Oh, where, oh, where can he be?
With his ears cut short and his tail cut long,
Oh, where, oh, where is he?

Hark! Hark!

Hark! Hark—the dogs do bark
The beggars are come to town.
Some in rags and some in tags,
And one in a velvet gown.

Old Mother Witch

Old Mother Witch,
Couldn't sew a stitch,
Picked up a penny
And thought she was rich.

I Love Sixpence

I love sixpence, a jolly, jolly sixpence,
   I love sixpence as my life;
I spent a penny of it, I spent a penny of it,
   I took a penny home to my wife.

Oh, my little fourpence, a jolly, jolly fourpence,
   I love fourpence as my life;
I spent twopence of it, I spent twopence of it,
   And I took twopence home to my wife.

Tom He Was a Piper's Son

Tom he was a piper's son,
He learned to play when he was young,
But all the tune that he could play
Was "Over the hills and far away."

Now Tom with his pipe made such a noise
That he pleased both the girls and the boys,
And they all stopped to hear him play
"Over the hills and far away."

He met old dame Trot with a basket of eggs;
He used his pipe, and she used her legs.
She danced about till the eggs were all broke;
She began to fret, but he laughed at the joke.

He saw a cross fellow beating an ass,
Heavy laden with pots, pans, dishes and glass;
He took out his pipe and played them a tune,
And the Jackass's load was lightened full soon.

If All the Seas Were One Sea

If all the seas were one sea,
   What a GREAT sea that would be!
And if all the trees were one tree,
   What a GREAT tree that would be!
And if all the axes were one axe,
   What a GREAT axe that would be!
And if all the men were one man,
   What a GREAT man that would be!
And if the GREAT man took the GREAT axe,
   And cut down the GREAT tree,
And let it fall into the GREAT sea,
   What a splish-splash THAT would be!

The Queen of Hearts

The Queen of Hearts
She made some tarts,
All on a summer's day;
The Knave of Hearts
He stole those tarts,
And took them clean away.

The King of Hearts
Called for the tarts,
And beat the Knave full sore;
The Knave of Hearts
Brought back the tarts,
And vowed he'd steal no more.

There Was an Old Woman

There was an old woman
   Who lived in a shoe;
She had so many children
   She didn't know what to do;

So she gave them
   Some broth without any bread,
Then whipped them all
   Soundly and put them to bed.

Ding, Dong, Bell

Ding, dong, bell,
Pussy's in the well.
Who put her in?
Little Tommy Green.
Who pulled her out?
Little Tommy Trout.

What a naughty
    boy was that,
To try to drown
    poor Pussy Cat!

Old Mother Hubbard

Old Mother Hubbard
Went to the cupboard,
   To give her poor dog a bone;
But when she got there
The cupboard was bare,
   And so the poor dog had none.

She went to the baker's
   To buy him some bread;
When she came back
   The dog was dead.

She went to the undertaker's
   To buy him a coffin;
When she got back
   The dog was laughing.

She took a clean dish
   To get him some tripe;
When she came back
   He was smoking a pipe.

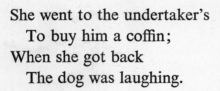

She went to the alehouse
To get him some beer;
When she came back
The dog sat in a chair.

She went to the tavern
For white wine and red;
When she came back
The dog stood on his head.

She went to the hatter's
To buy him a hat;
When she came back
He was feeding the cat.

She went to the barber's
To buy him a wig;
When she came back
He was dancing a jig.

She went to the fruiterer's
To buy him some fruit;
When she came back
He was playing the flute.

She went to the tailor's
  To buy him a coat;
When she came back
  He was riding a goat.

    She went to the cobbler's
      To buy some shoes;
    When she came back
      He was reading the news.

She went to the sempster's
  To buy him some linen;
When she came back
  The dog was a-spinning.

    She went to the hosier's
      To buy him some hose;
    When she came back
      He was dressed in his clothes.

The dame made a curtsy,
  The dog made a bow;
The dame said, "Your servant,"
  The dog said, "Bow-wow."

I Had a Little Hen

I had a little hen;
   The prettiest ever seen;
She washed me the dishes,
   And kept the house clean.
She went to the mill
   To fetch me some flour,
She brought it home in
   Less than an hour.
She baked me my bread,
   She brew'd me my ale.
She sat by the fire
   And told me many a fine tale.

Goosie, Goosie, Gander

Goosie, Goosie, Gander,
Where do you wander?
Upstairs and downstairs
And in my lady's chamber.

There I met an old man
That wouldn't say his prayers;
I took him by the left leg,
And threw him down the stairs.

Little Robin Redbreast

Little Robin Redbreast jump'd upon a wall,
Pussy cat jump'd after him, and almost got a
   fall;
Little Robin chirp'd and sang, and what did
   Pussy say?
Pussy said "Mew" and Robin jump'd away.

The North Wind

The north wind doth blow,
We soon shall have snow,
And what will poor Robin do then?
   Poor thing!

He'll sit in a barn,
To keep himself warm,
And hide his head under his wing:
   Poor thing!

There Was a Fat Man
of Bombay

There was a fat man of Bombay,
Who was smoking one sun-shiny day;
When a bird called a snipe
Flew away with his pipe,
Which vexed the fat man of Bombay.

There Was a Man
of Our Town

There was a man of our town
And he was wondrous wise.
He jumped into a quickset hedge,
And scratched out both his eyes;
But when he saw his eyes were out,
With all his might and main
He jumped into another hedge,
And scratched 'em in again.

The Man in the Moon

The man in the moon
Got up too soon
To ask the way to Norwich.

He went by the south,
And burnt his mouth
With supping cold peas-porridge.

One Misty, Moisty Morning

One misty, moisty morning,
    When cloudy was the weather,
There I met an old man
    Clothed all in leather.
He began to compliment
    And I began to grin,
Clothed all in leather,
    With cap under his chin,—
How do you do, and how do you do,
    And how do you do again?

Doctor Fostor
Went to Glo'ster

Doctor Fostor went to Glo'ster
  In a shower of rain;
He stepped in a puddle
  Up to the middle,
And never went there again.

Pippen Hill

As I was going up Pippen Hill,
  Pippen Hill was dirty;
There I met a pretty Miss,
  And she dropped me a curtsy.

Little Miss, pretty Miss,
  Blessings light upon you;
If I had half-a-crown a day
  I'd spend it all upon you.

Tweedledum and Tweedledee

Tweedledum and Tweedledee
   Resolved to have a battle,
For Tweedledum said Tweedledee
   Had spoiled his nice new rattle.

Just then flew by a monstrous crow,
   As big as a tar barrel,
Which frightened both the heroes so,
   They quite forgot their quarrel.

Burnie Bee

Burnie bee, burnie bee,
Tell me when your wedding be?
If it be to-morrow day,
Take your wings and fly away.

Fa, Fe, Fi, Fo, Fum!

Fa, Fe, Fi, Fo, Fum!
I smell the blood of an Englishman:
Be he alive or be he dead,
I'll grind his bones to make me bread.

The Old Woman of Leeds

There was an old woman of Leeds,
Who spent all her time in good deeds;
   She worked for the poor
   Till her fingers were sore,
This pious old woman of Leeds!

Tommy Snooks

As Tommy Snooks and Bessy Brooks
   Were walking out one Sunday,
Says Tommy Snooks to Bessy Brooks,
   "Wilt marry me on Monday?"

A Little Man

There was a little man, and he had a little gun,
  And his bullets were made of lead, lead,
    lead;
He went to the brook, and saw a little duck,
  And shot it right through the head, head,
    head.

He carried it home to his old wife Joan,
  And bade her a fire to make, make, make.
To roast the little duck he had shot in the
    brook,
  And he'd go and fetch the drake, drake,
    drake.

The drake was a-swimming with his curly tail;
  The little man made it his mark, mark, mark.
He let off his gun, but he fired too soon,
  And the drake flew away with a quack,
    quack, quack.

Why May Not I Love Johnny?

Johnny shall have a new bonnet,
　And Johnny shall go to the fair,
And Johnny shall have a blue ribbon
　To tie up his bonny brown hair.

And why may not I love Johnny?
　And why may not Johnny love me?
And why may not I love Johnny
　As well as another body?

And here's a leg for a stocking,
　And here's a foot for a shoe,
And he has a kiss for his daddy,
　And two for his mammy, I trow.

And why may not I love Johnny?
　And why may not Johnny love me?
And why may not I love Johnny
　As well as another body?

The Bells of London

Gay go up and gay go down,
To ring the bells of London town.

Halfpence and farthings,
Say the bells of St. Martin's.

Oranges and lemons,
Say the bells of St. Clement's.

Pancakes and fritters,
Say the bells of St. Peter's.

Two sticks and an apple,
Say the bells of Whitechapel.

Kettles and pans,
Say the bells of St. Ann's.

You owe me ten shillings,
Say the bells of St. Helen's.

When will you pay me?
Say the bells of Old Bailey.

When I grow rich,
Say the bells of Shoreditch.

Pray when will that be?
Say the bells of Stepney.

I am sure I don't know,
Says the great bell of Bow.

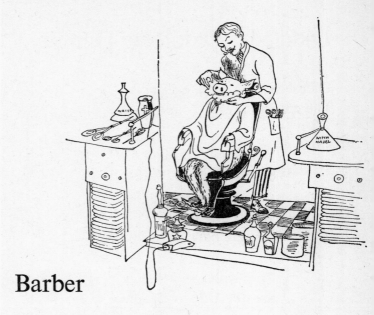

Barber

Barber, barber, shave a pig.
How many hairs will make a wig?
Four and twenty; that's enough.
Give the barber a pinch of snuff.

A Cock and Bull Story

The cock's on the housetop blowing his horn;
The bull's in the barn a-threshing of corn;
The maids in the meadows are making of hay;
The ducks in the river are swimming away.

Diddledy, Diddledy, Dumpty

Diddledy, diddledy, dumpty;
The cat ran up the plum tree.
  I'll lay you a crown
  I'll fetch you down;
So diddledy, diddledy, dumpty.

The Flying Pig

Dickory, dickory, dare,
The pig flew up in the air;
The man in brown soon brought him down,
  Dickory, dickory, dare.

Bandy Legs

As I was going to sell my eggs
I met a man with bandy legs,
Bandy legs and crooked toes;
I tripped up his heels, and he fell on his nose.

My Dear, Do You Know

My dear, do you know
How, a long time ago,
Two poor little children,
Whose names I don't know,
Were stolen away, on a fine summer's day,
And left in a wood, as I've heard people say?

And when it was night,
So sad was their plight,
The sun it went down,
And the moon gave no light.
They sobbed and they sighed, and they bitterly
cried,
And the poor little things, they lay down and
died.

And when they were dead,
The Robins so red
Brought strawberry leaves
And over them spread:
And all the day long
They sung them this song:

"Poor babes in the wood!
    Poor babes in the wood!
And don't you remember the
    Babes in the wood?"

Wee Willie Winkie

Wee Willie Winkie runs through the town,
    Upstairs and downstairs in his nightgown,
Rapping at the window, crying at the lock,
    "Are the children in their beds, for now
        it's eight o'clock?"

A Frog He Would A-wooing Go

A frog he would a-wooing go,
  Heigho, says Rowley:
Whether his mother would let him or no;
With a rowley powley, gammon and spinach,
Heigho, says Anthony Rowley.

So off he marched with his opera hat,
  Heigho, says Rowley,
And on the road he met with a rat,
With a rowley powley, gammon and spinach,
Heigho, says Anthony Rowley.

"Pray, Mr. Rat, will you go with me?"
  Heigho, says Rowley,
"Kind Mrs. Mousey for to see?"
With a rowley powley, gammon and spinach,
Heigho, says Anthony Rowley.

When they came to the door of Mousey's hall
   Heigho, says Rowley,
They gave a loud knock and they gave a loud
   call,
With a rowley powley, gammon and spinach,
Heigho, says Anthony Rowley.

"Pray, Mrs. Mouse, are you within?"
   Heigho, says Rowley;
"Yes, kind sir, I am sitting to spin,"
With a rowley powley, gammon and spinach,
Heigho, says Anthony Rowley.

"Pray, Mrs. Mouse, will you give us some
   beer?"
   Heigho, says Rowley;
"For Froggy and I are fond of good cheer,"
With a rowley powley, gammon and spinach,
Heigho, says Anthony Rowley.

Now while they were all merry-making,
  Heigho, says Rowley,
The cat and her kittens came tumbling in,
With a rowley powley, gammon and spinach,
Heigho, says Anthony Rowley.

The cat she seized the rat by the crown,
  Heigho, says Rowley,
The kittens they pulled the little mouse down,
With a rowley powley, gammon and spinach,
Heigho, says Anthony Rowley.

This put Mr. Frog in a terrible fright,
  Heigho, says Rowley,
He took up his hat and he wished them good-
    night,
With a rowley powley, gammon and spinach,
Heigho, says Anthony Rowley.

But as Froggy was crossing over a brook,
  Heigho, says Rowley,
A lily-white duck came and gobbled him up,
With a rowley powley, gammon and spinach,
Heigho, says Anthony Rowley.

So there was an end of one, two, three,
  Heigho, says Rowley,
The Rat, the Mouse, and the little Frog-ee!
With a rowley, powley, gammon and spinach,
Heigho, says Anthony Rowley.

Little Jenny Wren

Little Jenny Wren fell sick,
　　Upon a time;
In came Robin Redbreast
　　And brought her cake and wine.

"Eat well of my cake, Jenny,
　　Drink well of my wine."
"Thank you, Robin, kindly,
　　You shall be mine."

Jenny she got well,
　　And stood upon her feet,
And told Robin plainly
　　She loved him not a bit.

Robin being angry,
　　Hopped upon a twig,
Saying, "Out upon you! Fie upon you!
　　Bold-faced jig!"

The Death and Burial of Poor Cock Robin

Who killed Cock Robin?
"I," said the sparrow,
"With my little bow and arrow,
I killed Cock Robin."

Who saw him die?
"I," said the fly,
"With my little eye,
I saw him die."

Who caught his blood?
"I," said the fish,
"With my little dish,
I caught his blood."

Who'll make his shroud?
"I," said the beetle,
"With my thread and needle.
I'll make his shroud."

There Was a Monkey

There was a monkey climbed up a tree,
When he fell down, then down fell he.

There was a crow sat on a stone,
When he was gone, then there was none.

There was an old wife did eat an apple,
When she had ate two, she had ate a couple.

There was a horse going to the mill,
When he went on, he stood not still.

There was a butcher cut his thumb,
When it did bleed, then blood did come.

There was a lackey ran a race,
When he ran fast, he ran apace.

There was a cobbler clouting shoon,
When they were mended, they were done.

There was a chandler making candle,
When he them strip, he did them handle.

There was a navy went into Spain,
When it returned, it came again.

Mary's Canary

Mary had a pretty bird,
   Feathers bright and yellow;
Slender legs—upon my word,
   He was a pretty fellow.

The sweetest note he always sung,
   Which much delighted Mary;
She often, where the cage was hung,
   Sat hearing her canary.

When Jenny Wren Was Young

'Twas once upon a time, when Jenny Wren was
    young,
So daintily she danced and so prettily she
    sung,
Robin Redbreast lost his heart, for he was a
    gallant bird.
So he doffed his hat to Jenny Wren, requesting
    to be heard.

"Oh, dearest Jenny Wren, if you will but be
  mine,
You shall feed on cherry pie and drink new
  currant wine,
I'll dress you like a goldfinch or any peacock
  gay,
So, dearest Jen, if you'll be mine, let us appoint
  the day."

Jenny blushed behind her fan and thus de-
  clared her mind:
"Since, dearest Bob, I love you well, I'll take
  your offer kind.
Cherry pie is very nice and so is currant wine,
But I must wear my plain brown gown and
  never go too fine."

PART TWO

Mother Goose's
Favorite Alphabet Poems and
Rhymes about Counting,
the Days, the Months,
and the Weather

The Alphabet

A, B, C, and D,
Pray, playmates, agree.
E, F, and G,
Well, so it shall be.
J, K, and L,
In peace we will dwell.
M, N, and O,
To play let us go.
P, Q, R, and S,
Love may we possess.
W, X, and Y,
Will not quarrel and die.
Z, and ampersand,
Go to school at command.

A Was An Apple-Pie

A was an apple-pie

B bit it, C cut it, D dealt it,

E enjoyed it, F fought for it,

G got it, H hoped for it,

I inquired about it,

J jumped on it, K kept it,

L longed for it, M mourned for it,

N nodded at it, O opened it,

P peeped in it, Q quartered it,

R ran for it, S sat on it, T took it,

U upset it, V viewed it, W wanted it,

X, Y, Z, and & all wished

for a piece in hand.

One, Two, Buckle My Shoe

1-2

One, two, buckle my shoe;

3-4

Three, four, knock at the door;

5-6

Five, six, pick up sticks;

7-8

Seven, eight, lay them straight;

9-10

Nine, ten, a good, fat hen;

11-12

Eleven, twelve, dig and delve;

13-14

Thirteen, fourteen, maids a-courting;

15-16

Fifteen, sixteen, maids in the kitchen;

17-18

Seventeen, eighteen, maids a-waiting;

19-20

Nineteen, twenty, my plate's empty.

One, Two, Three

One, two, three, four, five,
Once I caught a fish alive.
Six, seven, eight, nine, ten,
But I let it go again.
Why did you let it go?
Because it bit my finger so.
Which finger did it bite?
The little one upon the right.

Play Days

How many days has my baby to play?
Saturday, Sunday, Monday,
Tuesday, Wednesday, Thursday, Friday,
Saturday, Sunday, Monday.

A Week of Birthdays

Monday's child is fair of face,
Tuesday's child is full of grace,
Wednesday's child is full of woe,
Thursday's child has far to go,
Friday's child is loving and giving,
Saturday's child works hard for its living,
But the child that's born on the Sabbath day
Is bonny and blithe, and good and gay.

Fingernails

Cut them on Monday, you cut them for health;
Cut them on Tuesday, you cut them for wealth;
Cut them on Wednesday, you cut them for
    news;
Cut them on Thursday, a new pair of shoes;
Cut them on Friday, you cut them for sorrow;
Cut them on Saturday, see your true love to-
    morrow;
Cut them on Sunday, ill luck will be with you
    all the week.

Sneezing

If you sneeze on Monday, you sneeze for
   danger;
Sneeze on a Tuesday, kiss a stranger;
Sneeze on a Wednesday, sneeze for a letter;
Sneeze on a Thursday, something better.
Sneeze on a Friday, sneeze for sorrow;
Sneeze on a Saturday, joy to-morrow.

Solomon Grundy

Solomon Grundy,
Born on a Monday,
Christened on Tuesday,
Married on Wednesday,
Took ill on Thursday,
Worse on Friday,
Died on Saturday,
Buried on Sunday,
This is the end
Of Solomon Grundy.

The Wind

When the wind is in the East,
'Tis neither good for man nor beast;
When the wind is in the North,
The skillful fisher goes not forth;
When the wind is in the South,
It blows the bait in the fishes' mouth;
When the wind is in the West,
Then 'tis at the very best.

Bees

A swarm of bees in May
Is worth a load of hay;
A swarm of bees in June
Is worth a silver spoon;
A swarm of bees in July
Is not worth a fly.

The Months

Thirty days hath September,
April, June, and November;
All the rest have thirty-one
Except the second month alone
Which hath but twenty-eight in fine
Till leap-year makes it twenty-nine.

The North Winds

Cold and raw the north winds blow,
  Bleak in the morning early;
All the hills are covered with snow,
  And winter's now come fairly.

When the Days Lengthen

When the days begin to lengthen,
The cold begins to strengthen.

May Flowers

March winds and April showers
Bring forth May flowers.

One, He Loves

One, he loves; two, he loves;
Three, he loves, they say;
Four, he loves with all his heart;
Five, he casts away.
Six, he loves; seven, she loves;
Eight, they both love.
Nine, he comes; ten, he tarries;
Eleven, he courts; twelve, he marries.

PART THREE

Mother Goose's Favorite
Puzzles, Games, Tongue-twisters
and Wise Sayings

A Candle

Little Nancy Etticoat,
In a white petticoat
And a red nose;
The longer she stands,
The shorter she grows.

A Star

Higher than a house, higher than a tree,
Oh! whatever can that be?

Pat-a-cake, Pat-a-cake

Pat-a-cake, Pat-a-cake, Baker's man.
Bake me a cake as quick as you can.
Pat it and dot it and mark it with a "T"
And bake it in the oven for baby and me.

Dance, Thumbkin, Dance

Dance, Thumbkin, dance;
                    (*move thumb*)
Dance, ye merrymen, everyone.
                    (*move all fingers*)
For Thumbkin, he can dance alone,
                    (*move thumb alone*)
Thumbkin, he can dance alone.
                    (*move thumb alone*)
Dance, Foreman, dance,
                    (*move first finger*)
Dance, ye merrymen, everyone.
                    (*move all fingers*)
But Foreman, he can dance alone,
                    (*move first finger*)
Foreman, he can dance alone.
                    (*move first finger*)
Dance, Longman, dance,
                    (*move second finger*)
Dance, ye merrymen, everyone.
                    (*move all fingers*)
For Longman, he can dance alone,
                    (*move second finger*)

Longman, he can dance alone.
>> (*move second finger*)
Dance, Ringman, dance,
>> (*move third finger*)
Dance, ye merrymen, dance.
>> (*move all fingers*)
But Ringman cannot dance alone,
>> (*move third finger*)
Ringman, he cannot dance alone.
>> (*move third finger*)
Dance, Littleman, dance,
>> (*move fourth finger*)
Dance, ye merrymen, dance.
>> (*move all fingers*)
But Littleman, he can dance alone,
>> (*move fourth finger*)
Littleman, he can dance alone.
>> (*move fourth finger*)

This Little Pig

This little Pig went to Market,
This little Pig stayed Home,
This little Pig had Roast Beef,
This little Pig had none,
This little Pig cried wee, wee, wee,
All the way home.

Brow Brinky

Brow brinky, Eye winky,
Chin choppy, Nose noppy,
Cheek cherry, Mouth merry.

Let Us Go to the Wood

SONG SET TO FIVE TOES.

1. Let us go to the wood, said this pig;
2. What to do there? says that pig;
3. To look for my mother, says this pig;
4. What to do with her? says that pig;
5. Kiss her, kiss her, says this pig.

This Pig Went to the Barn

1. This pig went to the barn.
2. This ate all the corn.
3. This said he could tell.
4. This said he wasn't well.
5. This went Week! week! week! over the door
   sill.

Here Sits the Lord Mayor

Here sits the Lord Mayor,	[*forehead*]
Here sits his two men;	[eyes]
Here sits the cock,	[*right cheek*]
Here sits the hen;	[*left cheek*]
Here sit the little chickens	[*tip of nose*]
Here they run in;	[*mouth*]
Chinchopper, chinchopper,	
Chinchopper, chin!	[*chuck the chin*]

Foxy's Hole

Put your finger in Foxy's hole,
  Foxy is not at home
Foxy is at the back door,
  Picking of a bone.

[*Holding the fist in such a way that if a child
puts its finger in, you can secure it, still leaving
the hole at top open.*]

This Is the Way

This is the way the ladies ride,
  Tri, tre, tre, tree,
  Tri, tre, tre, tree!
This is the way the ladies ride,
  Tri, tre, tre, tre, tri-tre-tre-tree!

This is the way the gentlemen ride,
  Gallop-a-trot,
  Gallop-a-trot!
This is the way the gentlemen ride,
  Gallop-a-gallop-a-trot!

This is the way the farmers ride,
  Hobbledy-hoy,
  Hobbledy-hoy!
This is the way the farmers ride,
  Hobbledy-hobbledy-hoy!

London Bridge Is Broken Down

London Bridge is broken down,
  Dance over my Lady Lee;
London Bridge is broken down,
  With a gay lady.

How shall we build it up again?
  Dance over my Lady Lee;
How shall we build it up again?
  With a gay Lady.

Build it up with silver and gold,
  Dance over my Lady Lee;
Build it up with silver and gold,
  With a gay lady.

Silver and gold will be stolen away,
  Dance over my Lady Lee;
Silver and gold will be stolen away,
  With a gay lady.

Build it up with iron and steel,
  Dance over my Lady Lee;
Build it up with iron and steel,
  With a gay lady.

Iron and steel will bend and bow,
  Dance over my Lady Lee;
Iron and steel will bend and bow,
  With a gay lady.

Build it up with wood and clay,
　　Dance over my Lady Lee;
Build it up with wood and clay,
　　With a gay lady.

Wood and clay will wash away,
　　Dance over my Lady Lee;
Wood and clay will wash away,
　　With a gay lady.

Build it up with stone so strong,
　　Dance over my Lady Lee;
Huzza! 'twill last for ages long,
　　With a gay lady.

Here We Go round the Jingo-ring

Here we go round the jingo-ring,
The jingo-ring, the jingo-ring,
Here we go round the jingo-ring,
With a merry-ma, merry-ma-tanzie.

Twice about and then we fall,
Then we fall, then we fall,
Twice about and then we fall,
With a merry-ma, merry-ma-tanzie.

Choose your maidens all around,
All around, all around,
Choose your maidens all around,
With a merry-ma, merry-ma-tanzie.

Ring a Ring o' Roses

Ring a ring o' roses,
A pocket full of posies.
Tisha! Tisha!
We all fall down.

How Many Miles Is It to Babylon?

How many miles is it to Babylon?—
  Threescore miles and ten.
Can I get there by candlelight?—
  Yes, and back again!
If your heels are nimble and light,
You may get there by candlelight.

[*Two children form arch with hands. Other
children pass under arch in line. One is caught
by sudden lowering of arms.*]

Here We Go round the Mulberry-bush

Here we go round the mulberry-bush,
  The mulberry-bush, the mulberry-bush,
Here we go round the mulberry-bush,
  On a cold and frosty morning.

This is the way we wash our clothes,
  Wash our clothes, wash our clothes,
This is the way we wash our clothes,
  On a cold and frosty morning.

This is the way we wash our hands,
  Wash our hands, wash our hands,
This is the way we wash our hands,
  On a cold and frosty morning.

This is the way we go to school,
  Go to school, go to school,
This is the way we go to school,
  On a cold and frosty morning.

Looby Loo

Here we dance Looby Loo,
Here we dance Looby Light,
Here we dance Looby Loo,
Dance with all your might.

Put your right hand in—and your right hand
    out,
Shake yourself a little, and turn yourself about.

Intery, Mintery

Intery, mintery, cutery corn,
Apple seed and apple thorn;
Wire, brier, limber-lock,
Five geese in a flock,
Sit and sing by a spring,
O-u-t, and in again.

Leg over Leg

Leg over leg,
As the dog went to Dover;
When he came to a stile,
Jump, he went over.

Peter Piper

Peter Piper picked a peck of pickled peppers;
A peck of pickled peppers Peter Piper picked.
If Peter Piper picked a peck of pickled peppers,
Where's the peck of pickled peppers Peter
  Piper picked?

Swan

Swan, swan, over the sea;
 Swim, swan, swim!
Swan, swan, back again;
 Well swum, swan!

I Would if I Could

I would if I could,
If I couldn't, how could I?
I couldn't without I could, could I?
Could you, without you could, could ye?
Could ye, could ye?
Could you, without you could, could ye?

A Walnut

As soft as silk, as white as milk,
As bitter as gall, a thick wall,
And a rough coat covers me all.

A Well

As round as an apple, as deep as a cup,
And all the king's horses can't pull it up.

Legs

Two legs sat upon three legs,
With one leg in his lap;
In comes four legs,
And runs away with one leg.
Up jumps two legs,
Catches up three legs,
Throws it after four legs,
And makes him bring back one leg.

[One Leg: A LEG OF MUTTON]
[Two Legs: A MAN]
[Three Legs: A STOOL]
[Four Legs: A DOG]

My Learned Friend Pig

My learned friend and neighbor Pig,
Odds bobs and bells, and dash my wig;
'Tis said that you the weather know;
Please tell me when the wind will blow.

A Sunshiny Shower

A sunshiny shower
Won't last half an hour.

Cock-crow

Cocks crow in the morn
To tells us to rise,
And he who lies late
Will never be wise;
For early to bed
And early to rise,
Is the way to be healthy
Wealthy and wise.

Good Advice

Come when you're called,
Do what you're bid,
Shut the door after you,
And never be chid.

Fears and Tears

Tommy's tears and Mary's fears
Will make them old before their years.

Needles and Pins

Needles and pins, needles and pins,
When a man marries his trouble begins.

He That Would Thrive

He that would thrive
Must rise at five;
He that hath thriven
May lie till seven;
And he that by the plough would thrive
Himself must either hold or drive.

The Cock Doth Crow

The Cock doth crow
To let you know:
If you be wise
'Tis time to rise.

Index

To First Lines of Poems

156

157